Uneven Terrain

Caroline Furr

TOHO
PUBLISHING

Copyright © 2020 by Toho Publishing

All rights reserved. Published by Toho Publishing LLC,
Philadelphia, in 2020.

FIRST EDITION

Cover design by Andrés Cruciani
Illustrations by Caroline Furr
Cover Art, *Salvador's Backyard*, by Caroline Furr
Original layout design by Tan Nguyen hyphenateagency.com
Layout by Ana Mitchell

Editor: Matthew Perez

ISBN 978-1-7336575-8-7 (paperback)

www.tohopub.com

to Libby

Fiction need not exist. Being busy with the truth seems enough.

CONTENTS

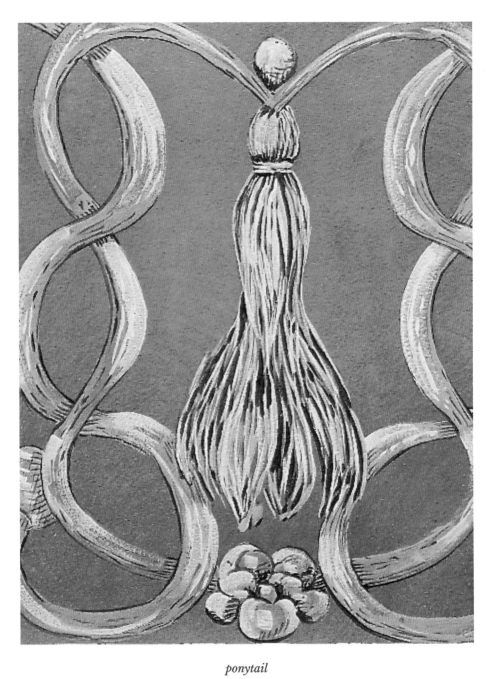

ponytail

METHODS OF HAIR REMOVAL

Josey was at the age when one finds oneself often before a mirror. The reason might be particular to the moment, such as an eruption on the end of the nose or the hairs on the upper lip, but in general this relentless examination was more an attempt to find—to see what was there of herself. Turning the face side to side, checking the planes, she gauged the symmetry and noted the tiny curve or miniature difference that rendered one side not quite the same as the other; she registered the parts that did not fit, filing away those places that would be under even more rigid scrutiny in the future.

She had just returned from the backyard, having been sent to the bathroom. It had been some sort of dare on Josey's part to present herself in high-noon sunlight with her lips brightly drawn on in a way that she thought canceled out her upper lip, now in the mirror nearly as red as the makeup itself and stinking from the chemical that had burned off the hated hairs. Her mother had glared into her face and saw she had plucked her eyebrows too, an act that had been often and clearly forbidden.

Josey hadn't been called from the house but had just ambled out and started a chatting conversation with her mother, who was hosing down a flower bed. A couple of times the dour woman glanced over. Then she said, "Let me see you," taking full measure of what had transpired on the girl's face. Josey thought she might get the water treatment, as she had come to expect whenever either parent was using the hose. But she was just told to go into the house and wash that stuff off her face.

The warm water and soap made her lip sting and flare up even more, and the eyebrows were lopsided and wrong. She thought she might cry and now felt completely empty looking at this strange face, not improved at all. Without warning, her mother's face appeared in the mirror, and as quickly and efficiently as Josey had ever seen her do anything, she grabbed her daughter's ponytail and cut it off cleanly at the rubber band.

Josey could never remember what happened after this, but she was sure it was mundane. She did inspect the jagged hair that soon fell free from the elastic, to frame her face in uneven lines, and thought about the ponytail, nearly certain that her mother had just thrown it into the trash.

AN IDEAL ARRANGEMENT

"Don't worry, it won't cost you much to get rid of me."

Her words were spoken into the windowpane, but Albert heard them clearly enough and crossed the room to touch her shoulder in a gesture of what he knew later was relief and gratitude. Before he could reach her, she had opened the door, and in her place was only a gust of cold air. Withdrawing his arm, he stood in the middle of the carpet while she stepped onto the terrace and without looking back walked across the lawn. He waited for her to return to the house for a coat, but she did not and soon disappeared into the trees.

After she was well beyond earshot, he thought about calling out to her or going after her with a wrap, but instead he closed the door and slid the small bolt firmly into place. As he stood poking the fire, he tried to calculate just what the cost might be.

He had never seen her before the day she, a single suitcase in hand, arrived with the parson. They were married in the main hall with his father and two servants as witnesses, and after the ceremony, he returned to his study. What became of the girl, even where she slept, was of little concern to him. He only cared that this meaningless act had fulfilled his promise—his father's concern being only with the land, not the happiness of any descendants, living or future.

It had been a year, and Albert's interest had not increased. He still knew nothing about her, but he knew something more of himself and now admitted that he was frightened of her. He sensed she wanted to complicate this simple life he loved, that she wanted to change everything.

She did not return for lunch. Often she visited the old lady in the property next to his, but when he telephoned and discreetly inquired, he was unnerved to hear that the women had never met. Lunch was one thing, he thought, but if she did not return for supper, he would be forced to confront her, so he dressed warmly and left the house in the same direction she had taken earlier.

By the time he approached the gardener's hut, he was in a mood of indignation at having his attention distracted from work, his orderly world of numbers, drawn to these outbursts that he resented and were becoming more frequent. He suspected she was trying to manipulate him into arguments, an inclination he could not fathom. Passing the hut, his speculation on where she might be spending her afternoons was disturbed by the sight of an old dog. He called to the animal, but it would not leave the porch.

Automatically he took the narrow path that led around the water's edge and puzzled his need of a wife, as he had on that day. A cold wind blew over the water, and he realized that she could not be out in a light dress in weather like this. As he turned to go back to the house, he saw the gardener pulling a cart of tools. He felt foolish being observed here at this time of day doing nothing and rushed on his way.

There was smoke from the gardener's chimney now, and as he stepped onto the lawn, he saw the man go around the corner of a hedge. Did the man have a wife? He must have, though Albert had never seen her.

That night she returned, wearing an old coat. When he asked where she had been and about the coat, she said nothing except they could finish their business now, and she boldly led him to his study. She left the house that night, walking away with her suitcase.

The following morning, he gathered the servants to inform that the back wood and lake were off limits. From the high road, people would sometimes catch a glimpse of her walking the old dog around the lake. She returned to her village life and Albert to his work, renewed in a sense and without a worry.

home sweet home

FAULTY APPLIANCES

Frank wasn't the sort of husband who forgot gifts. On all occasions Teressa was presented with a beautifully wrapped package of a certain size, and Frank would stand in front of her smiling a satisfied smile as she unwrapped it. The first gift had been on their honeymoon, and she thought the hand mixer must have been some sort of a joke, but over the years she knew that if it was a joke, it certainly wasn't a conventional one, for she now had eighteen hand mixers.

He had given her the second mixer on her birthday, which was barely two months later, and she had passed it on to a cousin who was getting married. When the couple had thanked Frank for the gift, she thought she would never hear the end of it; Frank was genuinely hurt that she had given this identical mixer away, so now she kept them all. She discovered they were easier to store if she kept them in their boxes, and most of them bore remnants of cheerful paper and bows. The cards that always accompanied the appliances she kept in another box under their bed. They were much less of a problem, and several times a year she did enjoy reading through them, even though they all expressed the same sentiment: "Hope you can use this. Love, Frank"—written in his large, childish handwriting.

Frank and Teressa entertained often, and they were acclaimed in their circle of friends for their tasty cocktails, so some of the kitchen gadgets had come in handy. Frank had an authentic dartboard that he had bought in England; it was installed on a wall next to a bar in the basement party room. Much later Sears was to stock the same dartboard, but at the time no one who hadn't been to England and gone to pubs had seen anything like it, and the men were impressed. Frank would stand behind the bar making exotic drinks, which he would then decorate with small umbrellas and plastic sticks with animal heads on them, which the women loved.

Sitting on the tall stools—within reach of the bowls of maraschino cherries, olives, and pickled onions just like in real bars—and watching themselves in the mirrored shelves with all Frank's special glasses made their friends feel very far from their own dreary homes, which were usually on the same block. Frank and Teressa even had fancy lights that winked on and off in pretty colors and a sort of music that only bars played. They were an extremely popular couple, which was fortunate because they moved a lot, and it was important to be able to make friends quickly to feel at home.

New friends, upon entering their house for the first time and before the magical qualities of the rumpus room were revealed, thought the house very strange. And people did call it "the igloo" behind Frank's and Teressa's backs. No one in Hanover Falls had ever seen an igloo except in movies and the *National Geographic* magazine, but they could imagine what one might feel like. Coming through the front door single file, hemmed in through the long hall lined in small boxes partially covered in wrapping paper with little bits of ribbon hanging down, meant entering another world, and no one had ever imagined people lived this way. Everyone of course compared notes, and those who had never been invited for darts, drinkin n' dancin (as their invitations read) were especially solicitous of the couple, for not knowing about the house firsthand put those people at a distinct social disadvantage.

darts, drink'n dancin

THE BELL

Wylie pressed his feet down as hard as he could, curling his toes deeper into the mud. The sun was hot on the back of his shoulders and the mud cool under his feet as he stood there wishing he could stay forever—just happy to be standing, like statues he had seen in books. Forever never did last long enough, and he started pulling his feet from the mud when he heard the bell.

She couldn't see him from where he was, but he could see her, standing on the porch and ringing the bell one last time before going back into the house. She rang it for meals and when she wanted him for something special. Wylie thought it was a good idea; he could be most anywhere and hear it. Once he had been down by the pond and heard it, heard it on the first ring and came running so fast he knew she had no idea he had been so far away. It was a little game he played, seeing how far he could go and still hear the bell.

He pumped some water into the bucket and stood in it until the mud fell away, rubbing his feet together and thinking that after lunch he would take Pepper down to the pond for a swim. Maybe catch a fish.

Wylie and his parents had lived on this farm for as long as he could remember. In fact he might have been born here. Now that his father was gone, he and his mother stayed on, raising chickens. They had layers, and he remembered her saying once that it was lucky they were layers because they would have starved if she had to kill a chicken.

He didn't know whether his mother missed his father; she never said a word about this. Once he had asked where his father was, and she had said she didn't really know but not to expect him to come home. That was all that was ever said, and Wylie didn't know what to make of it. He missed him, and once or twice, once even at school, he had cried when he thought about him, but he had a strong feeling that he was coming back. It would be just like before, and everything would be fine. When he thought he might cry, he would just tell himself that his father was coming home soon, and he felt better.

Wylie always ate a big lunch; it was his favorite meal. At night he was too tired to eat, and anyway it was whatever was left over from the day and cold, but lunch was fresh and hot, and there was plenty of it. He sat at the table with his bare feet resting on Pepper, moving them across the dog's thick coat and enjoying his lunch. He asked his mother what they made statues from, and she said big rocks, and they both thought this was the funniest thing they had ever heard and laughed until Wylie fell on the floor.

When he finished, he took his plate to the sink, put another piece of pie into some newspaper, and wandered into the yard with the dog. They both sat in the dirt while the boy ate the last piece of pie and thought about the swim. He wondered out loud if statues swam, and he could hear his mother laughing at this joke as he raced Pepper to the pond.

The coldness of the water surprised him; he had been in yesterday, and it hadn't seemed so cold, so he flipped on his back to catch some sun. Out of his slanted eyes, half closed against the bright sun, he saw a man walking along the hill that sloped to his house. He thought for a moment that it was his father, that he had seen a flash of red hair, so he quickly rolled over to swim to the bank, but a cramp doubled him, and he turned in the water taking in a mouthful of the pond, and then another turn and another mouthful and then another.

From just under the surface of the water, Wylie could hear the bell and then he knew that the man walking along the ridge was his father and his mother was calling him home.

big rock

DISCORD

How hideously delightful of you to say the work is your own when everyone here knows its provenance. You appear to us, covering neither your face nor pudendum, unacquainted with shame—what can you say for yourself, Simone?

Recalling the words Armand had spoken at the book signing downstairs, Simone's teeth gnashed, and she pressed her lips firmly together as if holding back an urge. At the reception, his little follow-on speech was riveting the guests clumped around him on the mezzanine, and as he strode toward Simone to deliver some coup de grâce, urge and manifestation came together to form a perfect spray of crab and champagne across A's fancy vest. Small pieces of half-digested crustacean fell from his elaborate hair, and his glasses had an odd green sheen to them. Simone thought it must have been the avocado toast she had noshed on before the event. The staff rushed forward to whisk Armand away and clean the floor as the horrified but untouched (and already not a little titillated) guests promptly departed.

A word about the vest. It was his signature item of apparel, and everyone had heard the story of *its* provenance: how his uncle Harry had worn it under his uniform throughout the war and, when the old man returned, given it to Armand, and now he too wouldn't take it off.

When it was returned from the finest hand launderer in London at considerable expense, driven to and fro, all on Simone's dime, A pronounced it shrunk. Even though everyone knew he had been puffing out for a year, the vest mishap allowed him some face saving, but also laid bare what had been for years a polite rivalry.

These public skirmishes continued and were the subject of many successful romans à clef, with characters even named Armand Duvall and Simone S, those two who never wrote another published word themselves but continued with their public antics to furnish the literary world with a gold mine of material.

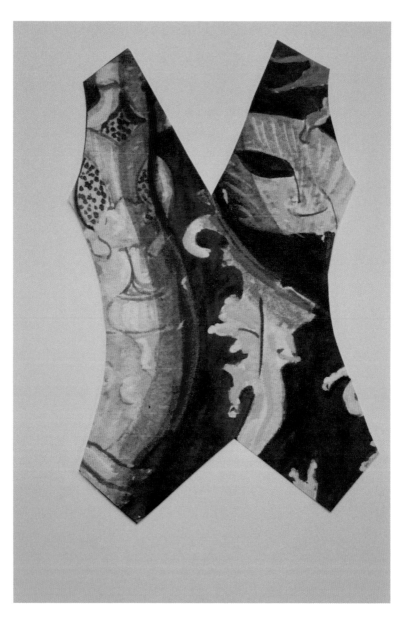

the vest

THE STORE

Rita was worn out. She would tell you that herself. Fifty years of working in her father's store and then going home to cook and clean for four boys and a rotten husband would do that to you. It hadn't been fifty years (she wasn't even forty yet), but there was something about the number she liked. A goal reached. She even told people she was fifty. As if anyone cared.

In the spring, the youngest of the boys would graduate from high school, and she had been saying to her father that when Ralph graduated—well, that was it. That's all she said, that that was it. Her father never answered her, never seemed to want to know what it meant, and most of the time didn't even look up when she said it.

Mr. Douglas, Rita's father, had worked in this store himself since he was a small child, had worked for his own father, who had started in grain and feed and then expanded into dry goods. When he was a teenager, he had built the addition on the back where they had moved the grain and feed business so they could expand. And before the old man passed, they had bought the small store next door and cut a wide-open door into the wall between the two buildings, stocking bolt fabric and work clothes in the new addition. What wasn't in the store the town of Kitchen's Corners didn't buy. Even catalog sales hadn't hurt them.

The old man died on a busy Monday morning as he was loading bags of feed onto a farmer's truck, and the store never even closed. He would have approved of that, and the town joked that Sam, Rita's father, had been born there, and Rita's generation said she had been conceived there. It wasn't so far off. The family had very little life away from the store, and Rita had hated it for as long as she could remember. Hated the smell of feed especially and wouldn't go to that part of the store unless she had to. Not that avoiding that section spared her from the smell, which permeated everything, especially themselves.

Sam was one of six brothers, and all of them had come up in the store. Two were killed during the war, and one, whom no one ever spoke of, was in detention somewhere. Elgar had hightailed it to Stowe right after graduation and then Philadelphia to become a doctor; he'd never returned. And then there was Billy, a little slow but there every day including Sundays, sweeping up and delivering unbreakables on his bicycle. None of the brothers had produced a known child other than Rita, so she held the obligation and high honor of continuing the legacy of the store. Sam didn't worry too much about the store staying in the family, what with Rita's boys, even though the first three had gone into farming and the youngest had already bought a bus ticket with his twenty-dollar graduation gift.

Rita didn't go on too much about hating the store, but last year her mother died, and Rita just about broke down, couldn't work for a week, and for the first time, Sam had to pay for help, and that just about broke him down.

The kid graduated. Rita was there in a new-looking dress, which made her look even more worn, with her father and husband. She smiled once when the kid came up to them after the ceremony. The three of them standing on the hot grass waving the program in their faces, and the kid ambles up in his long robe and Rita smiles. That was about it. They didn't go out for a meal or anything, just stood together on the grass for about fifteen minutes and then went their separate ways: the old man and Rita back to the store, the husband to the closest bar, and the kid, no one knew or cared more than he was expected at the store on Monday.

Douglas Feed & Dry Goods closed early on Saturday, at five. Sam had left earlier with a delivery out of town, so when five came around, Rita hung up her apron on the nail next to Sam's apron and went through the rooms, turning off lights and locking doors. From behind the counter, she took a small cardboard suitcase that had belonged to her mother, went out the front door, locked it, and walked down the street to the bus depot. She took the first bus out of town without asking where it was going, and no one in Kitchen's Corner ever heard from her again. The old man was furious, even contacted Elgar for the first time to see if he knew anything, but she never did turn up, and when Sam died, the store went to Billy and the three other sons who wanted to farm.

boys on the grass

A VERY PRIVATE MR. FINN

Every Friday morning Mr. Finn walked the two blocks to Main and Four Corners, where he bought food for his rabbits and transacted business at the bank. The entire outing took less than an hour and was his only time away from his mother's house. When he was younger, he had worked in a science lab, and since coming home and screening in the back porch, he had not once received a visitor. He rarely spoke and every day was the same routine, writing in notebooks and tinkering with bits of junk that came through the mail. At noon his mother brought the tray of boiled vegetables and put it on the hall table.

This was all common knowledge because the houses on the hill had a view of every move Mr. Finn made, down to his ritual of removing his socks at night, one foot slowly doing the deed for the other. He had never put up shades, so especially at night this extremely withdrawn man was an unwitting spectacle. The citizens of Kitchen's Corner by direct observation or gossip knew what Mr. Finn was up to infinitely better than they knew what their spouses did all day. But what exactly that was no one could really explain. Mr. Finn never indulged in the mindless picking and scratching that people enjoy watching other people do, and he had no semblance of a sex life, but the town was entirely fascinated by him and absorbed in his own total absorption.

All that changed one Friday, when Mr. Finn came into the bank and people he had only seen from their waists up ran out from behind their counters and formed a little circle, singing the happy birthday song. He was focusing on putting the new skirts, trousers, and shoes with the familiar heads and stood stiffly unresponsive to the singing and to the balloon that was put in his hand.

Completing his business, he walked toward the door, and when he glanced back at the group, several of the women squealed. On the corner a child loudly announced that Mr. Finn was holding a balloon, and he looked up at it with the same surprised expression as everyone else. A couple of young girls started laughing, and a car honked as the family inside waved all the way down the street. Stepping into Douglas Feed, the same song was sung, and he made out a banner with his name on it hanging over the bins of poultry feed.

With the sack of rabbit food and the balloon, he walked toward his house, but before he could open the gate, neighbors were standing around him, smiling and nodding. One woman handed him a cake, and another put a plate of cookies on the porch. The phone started ringing, and over the weekend, the town's devotion and excitement about Mr. Finn's birthday reached a positively hazardous pitch. He wasn't left alone except to sleep, spoke on the telephone to people he had never met, was spotted in two restaurants, whisked away to a movie, and on Sunday ate dessert three times. He thought he might explode.

Monday morning, he knew he wasn't the same even before he opened his eyes. His brain had refused to whir into its familiar pattern, and Mr. Finn decided he shouldn't get out of bed until his brain was with him, so he lay there for the entire morning. By midday everyone in town knew something was dreadfully wrong, and a neighbor was dispatched to the house to alert his mother.

From that day, he slowly disappeared in full view of the whole town. Voluntary starvation was what Dr. Berg wrote on the certificate, and when people asked Mrs. Finn about this horrible occurrence, she would respond blandly with what had been her son's last words, which were that he was looking for something and would get up when he found it.

lunch

LANDMARK

The man's hand fanned over the nearly perfect surface. "Wallboard is much smoother. What you want is plaster, and the man that does that work is on another job. Can you wait until spring?" Satisfied that a decision had been made, she left her number and waited until the spring.

Corrine had never lived outside a city, and although there wasn't much open space by country standards, it seemed to her a void, so after the first uneasy month on the land, she had decided to build a wall around the property. When she went to fence companies, the salesmen had usually recommended chain link, but it looked cruel and out of place, so she began researching walls at the library until one day she found the picture of what she had been seeing in her mind. It was low and curved as if it had erupted from the earth itself except for the blindingly white and smooth surface. The image was of a place she had never heard of and couldn't pronounce, but the wall was hers, what she had been looking for, and she instinctively loosened the picture from its binding and tucked it into the front of her blouse.

Walking from the library with the wall pressed against her, Corrine smiled and breathed a relief she hadn't known since moving to the farm. In her living room, she leaned the photograph on the mantle, supporting it with her grandfather's figurine of a mink. The shiny paper with the wall circling scrubby silver trees she didn't know gave olives looked at home behind the recumbent animal.

Now that the wall was a reality, the minks receded to sharp and hungry mouths she fed but no longer saw. During the last months of her grandfather's life, when they both knew he was dying, she had driven out from the city to be with him every weekend, and he had persistently tried to interest her in the animals. Then after his death, when she moved to the house, she obediently followed his detailed instructions on their care and feeding, but the image of crafty rats hiding in mink coats had stuck in her mind. She had rallied herself, almost not breathing, through the ordeal of scooping their food and cleaning the cages and becoming nauseated when they brushed against her. The animals frightened her, but she smiled now as she positioned the tiny china mink between the silver trees, closer and closer to the protecting wall.

On the day the man arrived, they stood together at the farthest point of her property, under an immense elm, and she shivered in the cool spring air and began to cry when she finally understood that he couldn't build the wall, that he only built interior walls and she should call someone else. Travis walked her back to the house and held the picture she released from the porcelain mink and drank tea and watched her eyes moisten again before he agreed to do the work.

During the preparation for the wall, the minks became so vague that she would often forget to feed them, and by the time the man had completed the metal skeleton of wire that would hold the plaster, they declined and had begun to die. Each morning she would place one or two of the tiny bodies in the waiting structure, covering them with leaves and later watching while the man plastered over another section. On the day the wall was completed and Travis had driven down the dirt road for the last time, she threw away the picture from the library. But the figurine, the mink on the mantle, stayed and Corrine dusted it and fussed over it like a trophy.

crafty

A STORY ALREADY TOLD

Grace had been sure of what she wanted in a husband since she'd turned sixteen and read a series of books on the subject of choosing a mate. Written by a popular author of the day (the president of some high-toned girls' school), the woman's opinions were soon Grace's own, and she went on endlessly in her slow, emphatic way telling everyone about the traditional qualities you should look for in a husband. That she waited until she was thirty-eight to marry didn't particularly surprise anyone, but her choice sure did. Some unkind people said she was just tired of holding out, and that was barely the beginning of those types of remarks.

Delbert O'Haverty wasn't quite twenty, and he didn't have any of the glorious qualities Grace had been talking about for years. He hadn't graduated from high school, didn't have a job or a car or a mother. People would laugh when they talked about Delbert; everyone thought he was a little slow, and they said he only had three things: a dog, a crazy father, and the reddest hair on earth.

Quick enough Grace stopped talking about the perfect husband, and very shortly after the wedding, much shorter than it takes any baby to get ready for this world, the first of the three boys were born. They lived with her folks until the boys started growing too big, and then they moved in with Delbert's father, who lived in a ramshackle place with an outhouse and no electricity on what used to be the outskirts of town and still was, what with progress moving the other way. Grace fought the idea hard at first, but there wasn't much of anything else to do, and after a time she accepted it. The boys were sort of raising themselves with the help of the dog, and it was about all Grace could do to keep enough food coming from the garden, so she came to feel that the isolation made the country way they lived less conspicuous.

Delbert finally landed some work. It wasn't much, but he was pleased with himself; he bought an old Ford and rattled around the country selling out of the car whatever he could lay his hands on, mainly paint and shingles. He would come home for clean clothes and then be off again for a week or more. There were a lot of wild stories about what Delbert was up to, and with the hair, there was certainly no mistaking him for anyone else.

After the three boys, Grace didn't get pregnant again until she was almost fifty, and everybody got a kick out of that. It was a scandal of sorts when the baby, a girl, was born and Delbert took the youngest boy and the dog and moved to Hanover Falls. Unkind people said that the old man had most likely tricked him into the marriage in the first place, and it was true that Delbert had never really taken on a fatherly role with the boys. And none of the kids had that flaming hair.

Grace changed after the last baby and pretty much stopped seeing people, wouldn't even visit her own family, and whenever people who used to know her from before would see her, which was seldom, even they sometimes didn't recognize her. She was worn and heavy, and that old confident, slow manner with the wild eyes behind it had all gone. The kinder people would say hello and ask about the children, and Grace would mumble something, but nothing much, and wander off as if she were listening to sounds no one else could hear.

People may have rarely seen Grace, but everyone knew the sight of the old man and the girl. They were everywhere— and everywhere together—chatting like a couple of monkeys. Almost every Saturday afternoon you could see them in the drugstore drinking malts after the movies, and a couple of times a week they would check out books from the library. The old man walked the girl to and from school every day, and in the summer months they fished the river and sold the extra catch on Main Street with little potholders the girl made. Oh, they were a real team. Even had matching straw hats.

When Grace's mother died, she and the girl came to the funeral, and after the service everyone gathered on the lawn for lemonade. People talked later about that day, seeing Grace and her daughter together. The girl must have been about fourteen then, sitting on the lawn, Grace silent as a stone and the girl lively as could be. And certain people liked to remind everyone that the girl went on and on to the others her age about the qualities a woman needed in a husband.

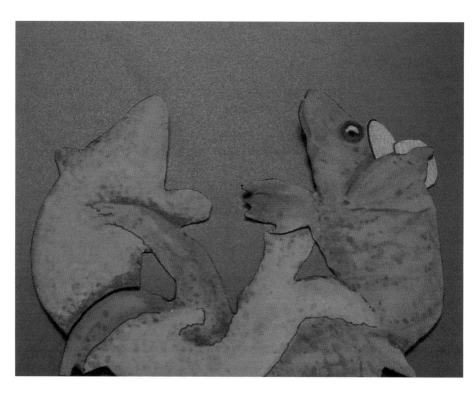

intertwined

LESS FUSS

Some years ago, an unknown writer had just completed his first novel, a mystery set in Spain. It had sprung quickly from his mind to the typewriter and then to a publisher he had picked without deliberation from a writers' directory, all this in a mere matter of months. While a worthwhile work, the book's good fortune was one of timing. And, of course, the sheer luck of finding its way to the right editor. All timing, all luck.

Marshall Kent—the now famous Marshall Kent—had a bad time with the second one, as often happens. The editor insisted on correct punctuation, which slowed down the rhythm of Kent's prose and took the edge off his unique style. It didn't jingle jangle along in the same way. Kent himself would read the improved work and couldn't understand the meaning or even remember what he was trying to say.

The correspondence between the two turned sour, and a new editor couldn't be found in time for the deadlines that had to be met, so the thing was published. The binding looked cheap, and no one seemed to care. Kent himself called it *the thing*, as if he'd given birth to a cat.

His publisher lost interest, and although Kent never slackened, the objective of another book, another chance at success, proved elusive. Soon he lost himself in expensive wine and chips. He wasn't so unhappy about it really. Less fuss.

notes for the next book

A FIRM RESOLVE

When Clarice was seven, her family moved to Hanover Falls and into a big new house with an attic, a basement, and a room of her own for each of the two girls. The entire family, anxious for the day to go smoothly, was waiting on the porch when the transport van finally arrived. Her father had even stayed home from work to help their mother and deal with the deliverymen. All the family was of a nervous type, and they were especially particular about the placement of themselves and their possessions.

Clarice had only moved twice in her life, once to this house, then again when she married Ogden, and these two events stood out in her mind like giant headlights in the night. She always used this phrase when talking about the two moves, and whoever was listening would invariable try and correct her by saying didn't she mean like beacons in the night, and Clarice would say no, she said what she meant and she meant giant headlights.

Even at seven it was noticed she was more peculiar than her older sister or her parents. She seemed the oldest and fussiest of the bunch, scolding her mother for misplacing things or crying, and everyone made it all the worse by indulging her in what they called a "natural maturity." Clarice quickly decided which room was hers, and every carton went directly from the van to the appropriate place, which she had marked with tape. The day was certainly not hectic by moving-day standards, but her mother still went to bed with a sick headache, and the next day they had to have dinner in a restaurant, which was another source of distress because eating out was something they did not do.

It was weeks before their mother came to their rooms to

measure for curtains, and she was surprised to discover Clarice's unpacked boxes neatly stacked in a corner with a blanket over them. It appeared that she was living out of a suitcase, and when she was directed to unpack, Clarice threw a little snit, talking fast about what a mess that would cause and how disturbing it would be. Her mother retreated from this tirade with another headache, and the subject wasn't brought up again, and gradually the boxes disappeared.

Despite the family intolerance for disorder, both girls did extremely well in school, and when the older sister graduated from high school, she went away to college in another state. Three years later it was Clarice's turn, and she decided she would rather live at home and take college courses through correspondence. That was how she met Ogden, who oversaw her test papers, grading her work and communicating with her about her course of study. It was fortunate they met this way because Ogden was completely in love before he discovered any of Clarice's oddities.

She amazed everyone who knew her by saying yes to his proposal but with one condition—that they would move once and never again, this after his refusal to live as a couple in her bedroom and his condition that they would have a long honeymoon. It was an austere wedding, and when they returned from the trip (Clarice said it was a trip and that was what it should be called), they lived in her bedroom so she could prepare for the next move. Ogden teased her about the pilgrimage, and people probably thought he was referring to the honeymoon, but what he was talking about was the impending move to his great-grandfather's house, barely five blocks away, where they would live without ever moving again.

He couldn't understand what all the fuss was about when he saw she didn't even have enough things to fill the station wagon. He hauled the boxes from her parents' attic by himself, old cardboard things with peeling tape and writing so faded no one but Clarice could make out the words. They drove the few blocks to their house, and she spent the day ceremoniously opening the boxes and placing the puzzling contents around the house.

In the early evening, she walked out the back and down the sloping lawn to where Ogden was burning leaves and sat in a lawn chair, watching him manage the fire. He heard her say it was the end of the first day and everything had found its place, and she had some things for the fire herself and would go get them. She returned with the worn boxes and stood calmly next to him as the fire blazed up with the boxes and finally burned out.

box of fire

CHISPA (THE SPARK)

Donna had been watching her mother take in clothes from the line when something in the sky caught her eye. It must have been a bird, but when she looked, all she saw was a spark falling against the winter sky. That couldn't be a star, she thought, too close to be a star, and you couldn't see a falling star in the daylight anyway, only at night and in the summer. She saw it go down at the far end of the garden, and when her mother called out to give a hand with the laundry basket, Donna ran like crazy, forgetting on purpose the oddest thing she had ever seen.

They had plans to enlarge the garden. It gave so much last year they got the idea they could sell the extra from a little stand on the main road. The money would be a real help, but the part that kept Donna awake at night was imagining the stand. All winter they kept their eyes sharp for bits of wood, and by spring they had saved enough money for nails and paint. On the first warm day, they staked out the new garden and at the farthest point were surprised to find a young bird sitting on a rock. It was too early for birds, especially young ones, and this one didn't seem to be about any business. He was just sitting, and they laughed as they told him it wasn't warm enough to be just sitting and then went on with their sticks and string.

During the first week of turning the land, Donna thought she saw the spark again and warily walked across the mud, trying to hold it in her eye. As she reached the edge of the plot, it seemed to have disappeared, and she turned to go back to her chores when she heard a *cheep* and saw him perched low on something sticking out of the ground. "You," she said, and went over to see what he was perched on. He hopped off whatever it was, and Donna couldn't believe her luck when she unearthed a pair of boots. They were a mess and almost too small but not too old, so she cleaned them up and wore them everywhere. When they went to town for seed, her mother bought a pair of red laces, and Donna cried she felt so happy.

One day she came up behind her mother in the soft earth and heard her talking to the bird. It must have been the bird because her mother didn't talk to herself, and the bird was very close, looking her straight in the face. Donna asked what she was saying, but her mother told her she hadn't said a word and especially she hadn't been talking to a bird. The girl watched them closely now but never heard her mother say anything even though from a distance sometimes she could see her lips moving, and the bird was always around through the turning of the land and the planting.

Several years passed until one evening when Donna showed up on the neighbor's porch wanting them to come over and check on her mother. Mrs. O'Haverty thought it funny that the girl wouldn't know if her own mother was OK better than people who had never shared more than a couple of words with them, who had never even been on the property, but they walked to the house with her anyway. Donna wouldn't go into the house but stood in the yard until the couple came out and said her mother was fine. Donna followed them back up the road as far as the vegetable stand and thanked them for coming over. There were some lively guesses between the couple of why anyone would want to keep thirty or more birds loose in a house. "What a mess," Mrs. O'Haverty said, and they looked back to see a light shining from the stand's small window.

birds in the house

WHAT BLONDES CAN DO

After you're up there a couple of times, it's no leap of imagination that you might need to explain to the blonde how to fly the plane. A dog and baby won't do you much good if someone would need to take over. If that happened, it would definitely be in the blonde's hands. They flew together every weekend, and she already knew how to tool the little thing around on a clear day, and once after a final loop over the field, he had said, "Land it," and immediately and wordlessly she had taken over. He was the one who had taken the controls back at the last minute and later felt a little sheepish because she was doing just fine.

Carlos had met her about a year ago as he was leaving a restaurant and an old friend from school had called him over to the round corner booth, where he stood the few minutes through introductions and small talk. It wasn't much, not memorable at all except in that funny way when later you know the moment you can't even remember has changed your life. And then a year later, he asked a shop girl for dinner, still without knowing it was the girl in the booth.

But Esmeralda knew exactly who he was as she quickly changed places with the girl who had started waiting on him, and at the end of helping him with the copies of blueprints for a new building, he asked her if she would like to have dinner when he picked the prints up at the end of the week. Friday. She said yes and immediately knew what she would wear: her white mohair coat, long black leather gloves, black crocodile shoes and bag.

Esmeralda was thirteen when she realized she could only escape her nothing town by going blond and had bought the peroxide from the town's only drugstore and two years later took a bus out of town and never looked back or even wrote a note home. She called it a fresh start and lived in a house with a sign out front that said, "Rooms to let, clean and respectable." She took a secretarial course, which was her education and finishing school rolled into one, and began working, using all her money on clothes and hair maintenance. Some people, women mainly, just know how to discover a new world.

Without calling during the week, he reappeared on Friday. It was raining and dark by the time he arrived, ten minutes before closing, but she had never lost confidence that he would be there. She didn't wait on him when he came in, didn't even look at him, but when he had picked up his blueprints, he stayed in the front part of the store looking at the drafting equipment. She joined him in her white coat, already buttoned, pushing the gloves up between her fingers, and they went out to his beautiful new car parked illegally in front of the store.

the blonde

THE PROMOTION

Marge was exhausted the morning after the party. She was never invited anywhere, and as she walked down the hall toward the office, she vowed that if she were asked again, she wouldn't go.

The door was ajar, and Mr. Fox was already there. In a lifetime of working for him, since she had graduated from high school, he had never opened the office himself. That had always been her job, but she hung up her coat, sat down at her desk as if nothing were different, and waited for him to speak.

It was a literary office. What she meant was that Mr. Fox was a literary agent, and he set a tone of being very careful with words. Because she was so anxious about saying something wrong, she rarely spoke at all. She had no idea what he thought of her or even if he was pleased with her work. Normally he communicated in cryptic notes written with a dull pencil that seemed at odds with his precise words, but Marge didn't give it much thought.

She glanced over and saw him kneeling beside a box of files and wondered if he was married. Her friends had teased her when she started working for him, but over the years, that stopped; she didn't really have friends now as the office took up most of her time, and when she went home, there was her mother to care for and the sweaters to knit. She was an excellent typist and an excellent knitter, and the sweaters were sold to a shop in California. She had never been to California and couldn't imagine going, but she didn't think much about these things either.

Her only regret, if you could call it that, was the impossibility of reading and knitting at the same time, so she and Mother ended up watching television every night. Vaguely she thought she might have had a different life if only she could have read more and maybe continued writing her stories; she might even travel to California and visit the shop that sold her sweaters. Years ago a friend had given her a book stand for her birthday, but it hadn't worked out, and she had gone back to television.

Mr. Fox turned with a blue file in his hand and laid it in the middle of her desk. "Miss Pearl, please respond to these letters and sign them under your own name. I will be away from the office for two weeks." Without another word, he took his coat from the chair and left the office.

This was very strange. It had all been strange. He had never asked her to answer letters, and the thought of signing her name to anything made her feel physically ill. Holding the file, she wandered to the window and stared down into the street until Mr. Fox appeared and got into a convertible that was waiting at the curb. A woman was in the driver's seat.

The car and the woman's hair were the same orange color, and in another instant Mr. Fox was beside her, kissing her and silently laughing, when the car lurched from the curb and sped away, the woman's swirling hair visible for blocks.

The file held dozens of letters addressed to Mr. Fox, and she took the first, which asked for a response as to what a person could do about a dog's tail bleeding because the animal beat it so hard against the walls and furniture. The letter was signed by Oliver Harkness, a person she did not know. After giving this problem serious thought, she carefully put Mr. Fox's letterhead into her typewriter and answered.

Dear Mr. Harkness,
Keep it bandaged, but in extreme cases, the tail must be removed.

And she signed her own name.

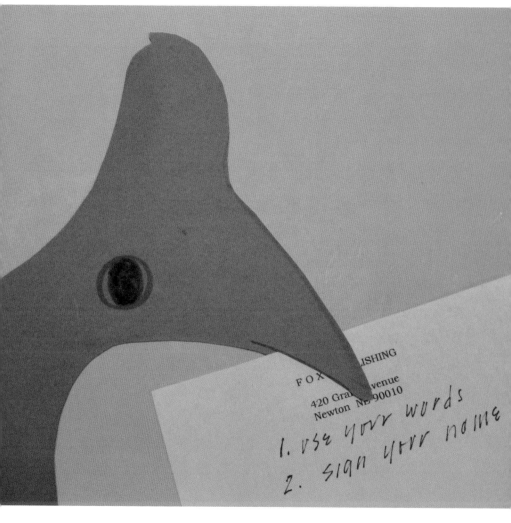

note to self

AN UNDERSTANDING OF SHAG

That's what she said, that he didn't really understand shag. And it was true that he had never had the ability to walk onto the new rug—or as he said, in it—without tripping. And so he had tripped backward and hit his head on the massive andirons.

The very ones the two men had just brought in from the truck, not even placing them in the fireplace, saying that the three other men coming to finish the job tomorrow would do that. Those movers had let themselves out, and he now stood in the unfinished room, watching them drive away, when he heard a click behind him and turned to see his wife. She did this often, was upon him soundlessly and quick.

It was she who said he had tripped. And he had, with the help of a little push and him down with a fall onto the big andirons that sat in the shag. Beautiful white shag with the red spot that they would never get out. Clumsy man making a big mess.

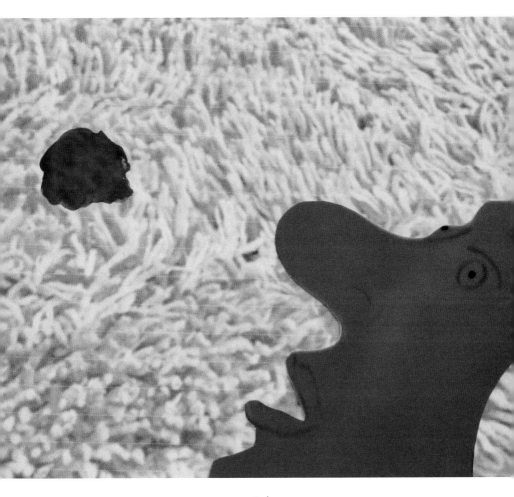

surprise

BOOK CHAT

This party—being invited and showing up—marked the end of Troy's long seclusion. There was music and booze and lots of dames in low-cut dresses. He felt alive in a way he hadn't in months, frisky and ready to take on the world. Block it's called, but without the added description of concrete or its unsuitable placement in the lower gut. But all that was behind him now, and he no longer kept to himself, especially at parties, where the innocent question of what he did made him feel a fury.

There were a few people there he knew, a past girlfriend or two, and one of them was saying that the woman across the room in the brown dress was also a writer. Eager to engage a fellow pilgrim in some light chat, especially now that the long dry spell was over, he gave her a quick sizing up. She wasn't really his type though, so he headed toward the bar, where he stayed the entire evening until he wandered into the kitchen and there was this woman in the brown dress at the sink washing glasses.

"I understand you are a writer."

The woman quickly twisted the faucet, but through the running water, he could hear the words: "Not anymore."

With the reflexes of a panther, he demanded that she repeat herself, and finding strange comfort in the familiar exchange, he sat down, lit a cigarette, and let out a giant exhalation of smoke, blandly asking if smoking bothered her. He waited until she had rinsed the glass and shut the water off to ask what he knew was his best question.

"And what was your subject?"

Millicent clung to the counter and said to the sink that she didn't understand the question exactly but what interested her was love, what she tried to express was love, and gathering a little courage from her noble theme, she approached him and from her purse took out a small comb with several missing teeth.

As she pulled the comb through her thin bangs, a dark hair fell on the table between them, and with the most contempt he had ever felt for anything, he flicked it away with his smoking hand.

"Ah yes, love. And what sort of love was it, were you a champion of the rough stuff?"

She shrunk away as he began to speak in ways that made her feel sick. He grew vile and loud, and she held onto the kitchen table with one hand and the damaged comb with the other as if his booming voice would blow her away if she let go of these two dubious supports. He lit another cigarette, her face dim in the smoke as he continued his ugly monologue.

He didn't enjoy the rest of the party and went home early in a cab. Slumping in the back and ready to be in bed, his attention was suddenly focused on the driver going a little too fast as the taxi swung around a corner to enter a high bridge. He rested his head on the cool glass of the window and glanced down the outside of the door to view a fire escape from above, the dark framework smaller and brighter toward the street. In that moment, he was sure he saw a cabbage smashed on the top landing, reminding him of news stories, and he turned away, even though the eyes of the cabbage had already seen him.

The next morning, thoughts of the stupid woman kept him from writing. Hours passed as he sat in front of the machine until his little finger jerked abruptly and, hitting the caps key, he typed out the words *MY THEME IS NOT LOVE*. Only briefly did he consider the meaning of what he had typed, and in the next moment, he was in a deep and dark place stacking blocks one upon the other.

the eyes of the cabbage

THE READING OF THE WILL

Gloria sat down and adjusted herself into a position she thought comfortable. She didn't want to fidget, so she concentrated on her toes pointing and flexing very slightly in the black pumps as the short man read from a book. When he had finished and joined the others at the end of the table, someone was at her side with a glass of water, and Gloria held it for a moment before placing it carefully in front of her. Then another man stood and began to speak, but she didn't understand what he was saying, and her attention wandered to the pattern of birds and flowers in the fabric of a nearby sofa. She thought it a feminine choice for this type of office and then realized she had sat there often without noticing the design of birds with elaborate plumage and crowns but, curiously, no feet. The slender legs pointed nowhere, like pirate stumps, and she frowned at such an odd omission as she crossed her ankles and pulled her own feet under the chair. The smell of coffee brought hope it would soon be over, so she could go home and lie on their bed in the cool afternoon light.

A low and serious voice spoke now, and she strained to hear his words but only became more aware of traffic in the street below and office machines on the other side of the wall, and she fixated on balancing these sounds. She watched her fingers twist a button on her jacket and then saw a gouge in the leg of the table. How could such a deliberate-looking cut have happened, she wondered, and feeling panic and embarrassment, she quickly looked away, her eyes searching the room for a clock but only imagining their own clock; he had always needed one to wake up as the light in their room was so dim you could sleep all day.

A man was now taking papers from his briefcase and one by one sliding them toward her, indicating with a small dot of his pen where she should sign. She opened her purse and took her own pen and signed her name until the stack of papers disappeared. When she replaced the pen, the closing purse made a sharp click, and Gloria's body turned toward the door, believing the sound had come from somewhere else. Now the men were standing together at the end of the table, and Gloria stiffened her back as if to rise also but instead slumped and crossed her legs, glimpsing the toe of her shoe, which was pointing in a mocking way to the deep cut on the table leg, and, with a peculiar gasping sound, began to cry.

birds

A PERFECT HOUSE

Rolly Petersen believed that buying a house that had been vacant for a substantial period, say six months, was simply smart business. He called it "the decent interval," and if asked why, he would explain how it allowed any ghost an opportunity to vacate the premises. The drawback, of course, was that the house felt even more empty. Most realtors used plants, freshly baked cookies, and open windows or well-lit rooms to say, "Welcome home!" But Rolly was less conventional. His approach was to use disparate items in odd places; a favorite was midsized blow-up deer in the bathtub. Often the prospective buyers wouldn't mention these items, and their silence convinced Rolly all the more of their merit in clinching the deal. He was also fond of Le Corbusier's phrase "machine for living," which most people were ignorant of and thought must mean a special new gadget somewhere, maybe the garage.

Corbu's words lingered as the couple walked through the rooms and admired what Rolly called levels and different zones and the two pools with their own, he said, pavilions. Sid and Ida felt entranced by the idea of a new life within reach, the idea and the life forming the interlocking parts of a well-run machine. They even asked if Rolly might leave the deer.

Witness here another heroic attempt to improve one's life by moving, this time to Phoenix, where they knew no one. The cost for transporting their extensive collection of specimen ferns, which they planned to install in one of the specially prepared pool pavilions, came to over a million dollars. So when the giant refrigerated truck's door opened and they saw that many of the plants had frozen and then turned a horrible color within seconds of being blasted by the 110 degree heat, it was not only the atrocious smell but the pathetic sight of their beloved ferns that made Ida throw up in the driveway. Something went wrong with the truck, the moving men said.

This wasn't the first unfortunate incident Phoenix had presented. On the second day, before any trucks had arrived, Sid and Ida had been daydreaming about their happy new future and moving the deer around the house to gain the most effect, when their asthma kicked in more severe than ever. And the moral here is there's a lot of no better and sometimes even worse in the attainment of one's dreams. Best to leave some dreams on the pillow.

a machine for living

DEBUT

Except for once in a piano bar when the microphone was passed around and earlier when singing in the church choir, which maybe didn't count because it was the junior choir and she had been twelve, except for those two experiences, Mira had never sung in public. Singing with a group, in the middle row, wearing a robe, really counted less than the bar experience, but she persisted in thinking of herself as a singer. She had gone to karaoke bars once or twice, but the pitch of the music was too high; she was an alto, and she couldn't keep pace with the jaunty arrangements. The "Tennessee Waltz," slow and a little awkward with the one piano, and the serious hymns were more her style.

But here she was fifty years later waiting to sing. After the Twin Tappers, she was to count to six and then come onto the stage. The twins were doing their individual taps, which meant they were about half through, and she felt herself sort of tapping along with them as much as she could in these new shoes, which were so tight and so high they made her feel a little dizzy. Suddenly the twins were skipping her way, waving to the audience, and she began counting as their full skirts brushed by her and she let go of the curtain.

The stage was brighter and bigger than it had felt at rehearsals, when people would come and go. She thought maybe they had turned on more lights, and looked into the audience, which she could barely see now. They were there; she heard coughing and a person laugh. She knew she was walking very slowly; she felt stiff as if she'd worked too hard in the yard and couldn't get anything to move the next morning. Things weren't right: she couldn't see and couldn't move and didn't have a sense of what was happening to her when she reached the microphone and took hold of that support with both hands and was reminded of a postcard someone had sent her from Venice with striped poles in the water to tie up boats. Someone offstage was hissing her name, and she looked over at him, wondering what he wanted. Did he want her to come back? But the music started, so she began to sing. It was a very small voice, and a man in the audience yelled, "Louder!" But her voice wouldn't make a louder sound and then didn't make any sounds at all.

When the music stopped, she knew her performance must be over, and she turned and walked slowly away before she was jerked to a stop by the microphone cord. She was still holding the mike, and the audience laughed.

Mira was mortified by this experience and didn't leave her house for a week; she even stopped going to church. All music now was just a reminder.

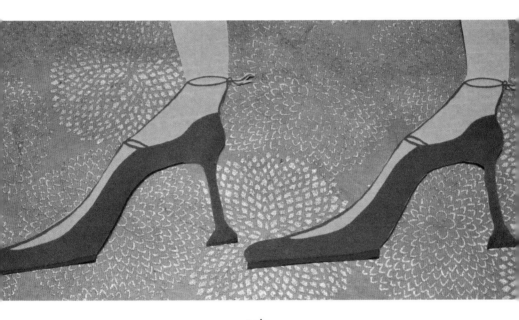

pain

A MISSING TOOTH

She was in the living room, making an inspection for dust and anything that seemed out of order, when she picked up what looked to be a chipped piece of plaster. "Sir won't like that, Missy," Lylee said in her high voice, as Missy looked down at the plaster again and saw it had probably come from one of the Chinese vases. Lylee could remember when a tradesman had once knocked over one of the vases and Missy had cried in front of everyone and had to be taken from the room. But Missy was as liable as anyone to knock them over, and Lylee was, after all, the true guardian of the valuable collection. She was the one who dusted them; she was the one who truly knew them and cared.

Standing between the vases and the men, she watched Missy go toward them as she was introduced to Inspector Vick. Tea was brought in, and Missy sat for another hour and told her story of where she had been yesterday afternoon from noon to three. As the interview concluded and the men rose to leave, Inspector Vick asked what she had in her hand, and without speaking Missy handed over the tooth of the now dead man.

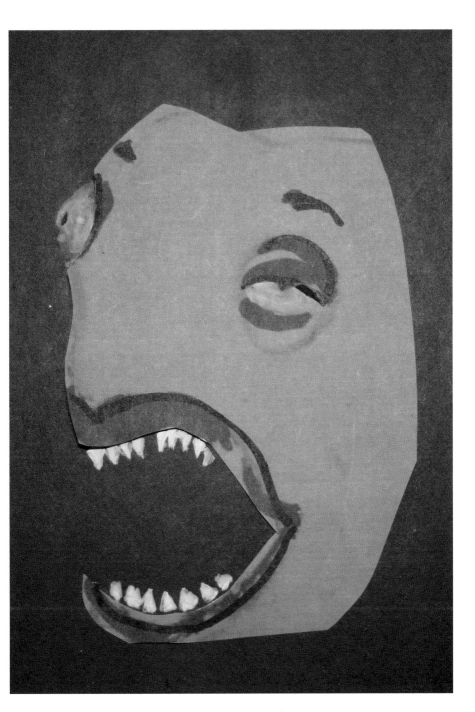

a missing tooth

TWILIGHT LANES

Those who had never particularly thought of him as the most clever of their group were properly humbled when the article appeared in a national magazine, even though *Home and Hearth* was not the sort of magazine any of them had ever read. They didn't really go in for reading. Bowling was what they went in for, and when Freddy came through the big double doors of the Twilight Lanes that Friday night, he had the magazine halved into his back pocket. He was purposefully late, and as he approached his friends drinking their beers, he pulled the magazine out and placed it on the bar.

"Hey, Freddy, what's this you have, thinking about getting some curtains?" one of them said, and everyone laughed until he opened to page 33 and they saw his picture staring back. The guys gathered in, looking at Freddy sort of smirking into the camera, wearing a suit his friends had never seen. His hair looked different too as if he had just pulled himself out of a swimming pool. He looked thin, and his nose looked sharp. But it was Freddy, no one doubted that. And behind him was a large picture of flowers.

It seems that after his day job delivering beverages for Standard Beverage, he had been cutting up pictures of flowers he had found in magazines and pasting them down on big sheets of newspaper. There was a flurry of questions and then silence as his friends waited for an explanation. How it all started when he was cleaning out his mother's garage and found all the magazines and thought it wasteful to just throw them out, so he had started cutting out all the flowers and, when he had done that, then haphazardly pasting them onto newspapers. Freddy said it had given him great satisfaction, and his friends looked at him as if they no longer knew him.

"What do you mean, great satisfaction? How long have you been doing this?"

And then Freddy continued with how all his spare time had been taken up during the past year with this cutting and pasting and how his mother had taken several and put them up in her living room, and one of her friends had called someone in store display and they had put some in their windows, and a New York store had used them and then an art gallery had called. And on and on.

No one had touched their drinks during this speech, and they all stood together now, apart from Freddy with the open magazine between them. Freddy was smiling, not a big smile but a small, more private smile. He looked satisfied; then he started up again with his plans for what he called, they thought he said, colleges, whatever that was.

The loudspeaker announced their lane was ready, and the men slowly took their beers and walked away, leaving Freddy and his magazine to follow.

collage

WEIGHING THE HEART AGAINST A FEATHER

Stacked up against the corner, sixty years of work didn't look like much, and Miss Iris said so as the moving man bent down to pick up one of the large boxes.

"What kind of work did you do?"

Her answer, as she went down the hall toward the back of the house, was for him to leave the red boxes; she would take them with her when she left.

The other men were hoisting a wooden chest onto the truck, and Charlie stood in the window a moment watching them before turning and following her. It was getting late; the job had taken longer than it should have, what with the old lady's reluctance to get down to business and Mel's boys happy to oblige her.

He heard the crash before he saw her and as he turned the corner into the kitchen almost stepped on her. She had fallen from a ladder while trying to unhook some holiday decoration, a tinsel angel, which was now lying on her chest. Oh God, he thought, as he bent over her with his ear against the angel not hearing a sound, then feeling for a pulse and realizing that she was very quickly and cleanly dead. He sat beside her, smoothing her dress, and remembered they were in a house twenty miles from town with a disconnected telephone. Why people did that before moving day he could never figure, and he picked up the hand not holding the angel and laid it across her waist.

She looked fine really; maybe she was relieved to not move anywhere, perhaps especially Hanover Home. As he examined a broken fingernail, a spider emerged from the tinsel ornament to make its way to a corner, and suddenly Charlie felt cold. As he was closing the window, he heard the men coming down the hall and jumped over Miss Iris to block the door, smashing into the three of them and knocking the youngest down and giving him a bad cut on the head. After they cleaned up the boy, they carried her upstairs and laid her on her bed, still holding the angel.

It didn't feel right to leave her alone, so the men sat on the floor around the bed and ate lunch while waiting for the person who was to fetch her and the red boxes, but when no one came, they loaded the rest of the furniture. It was dark now. Of course, the electricity had been turned off as well, and all they had were a couple of flashlights from the truck.

"This is crazy, Charlie. Are we going to wait all night? No one's coming for her now."

Mel's boys were getting hungry again, and the youngest one was bleeding a little from the cut. Charlie knew what Mel wanted to do, just drive off and deliver the furniture along with the old lady as planned. But Charlie wasn't so sure. If they did, where exactly would she ride? In the back with the furniture didn't seem right, but neither did the front, propped up between the boys. The whole business troubled him.

Finally Mel said they were going to deliver the furniture as planned, and Charlie could stay out here all night if he wanted.

He would stay. He didn't know what else to do, so they moved her back downstairs next to the red boxes, put the bed on the truck, gave Charlie a flashlight, and drove away. He felt a little relieved as the truck lights disappeared at the end of the road; his headache even went away, and he knew he should just settle in and get some rest. It would all sort out in the morning.

He took off his jacket and laid it carefully over Miss Iris and then propped himself against one of the boxes, taking a last look before clicking off the flashlight. Lying on the bare floorboards and watching the mulberry tree moving outside in the breeze, he thought he smelled the scent of baking, or maybe it was lavender, and he closed his eyes. As he fell asleep, his foot turned toward her and lightly touched the hem of her dress, but Charlie didn't notice that or her hand open to release the angel.

weighing

THE BIRTH OF LUGGAGE

In the southern coastal town of Grinza, the curious traveler can visit an early cave painting of what is clearly a bird carrying a suitcase. And a stranger papyrus document exists, which has been dated to the early Phoenician period: a diagram of how to pack a suitcase and what to take on your journey. So there was an early interest in the subject.

Ancient prototypes made of vegetal material produced unhappy results and obviously are no longer extant. Even the later improved ones constructed of mud lost their contents or were too heavy to move; and the mud, when set, would form a hard surface that had to be broken open with clubs, oftentimes destroying its contents. Then there was the general outcry from the sack-carrying populace: What need have we for such an invention!

Rain and snow proved unfriendly to early luggage, but papyrus schematics also show what appear to be handles and perhaps hinges, so advancement continued. The wheel was invented in 3500 BC, though the world would wait a long time to see their functionality in the transport of luggage.

Fits and starts all the way.

the birth

ACKNOWLEDGEMENTS

Thank you Matthew Perez for the essential and thoughtful work that is editing. And Editorial Assistant, Ana Mitchell.

Thank you Andrés Cruciani, founder of *Toho Publishing*, for this opportunity and your good natured guidance.

ABOUT THE AUTHOR

Caroline Furr was born in Oklahoma and completed her MA in sculpture in Los Angeles. She was founding director of The Children's Museum and has painted sets for TV and film. While living in Barcelona she collaborated with a furniture designer and a sculptor. She has had an ongoing exhibition history since 1974 and worked in surface design and interior design on the East Coast. Based in Philadelphia, the stories that began in Barcelona almost thirty years ago have found a home.
carolinefurr.com